D0001490

This edition published by Parragon Books Ltd in 2017

Parragon Books Ltd
Chartist House
15–17 Trim Street
Bath BA1 1HA, UK
www.parragon.com

Copyright © 2017 Disney Enterprises, Inc.
The movie THE PRINCESS AND THE FROG Copyright © 2009
Disney, story inspired in part by the book THE FROG PRINCESS
by E.D. Baker Copyright © 2002, published by Bloomsbury
Publishing, Inc.

Rapunzel's Challenge written by Lara Bergen. Copyright © 2013
Disney Enterprises, Inc. Based on characters from the movie
Tangled. Copyright © 2010 Disney Enterprises, Inc.

Cinderella: Princess in Disguise written by Lisa Ann Marsoli.
Copyright © 2013 Disney Enterprises, Inc. Based on the
characters from the movie *Cinderella*. Copyright © 1950 Disney
Enterprises, Inc.

Belle and the Perfect Pearl written by Ellen D. Risco. Copyright ©
2014 Disney Enterprises, Inc.

All illustrations by the Disney Storybook Artists.

All rights reserved. No part of this publication may be reproduced,
stored in a retrieval system or transmitted, in any form or by
any means, electronic, mechanical, photocopying, recording or
otherwise, without the prior permission of the copyright holder.

ISBN 978-1-4748-7818-0

Printed in China

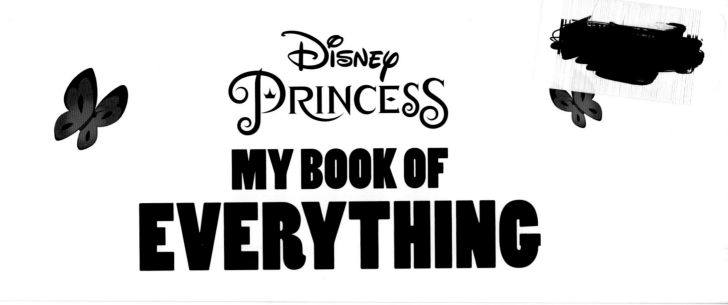

Disney PRINCESS
MY BOOK OF
EVERYTHING

Contents

PaRRagon

Bath · New York · Cologne · Melbourne · Delhi
Hong Kong · Shenzhen · Singapore

Rapunzel's Challenge

$\mathcal{R}$apunzel skipped along happily as Flynn Rider guided her through the forest. She couldn't believe it. For 18 years, she had watched from her tower window as magical lanterns floated up into the sky on her birthday. All her life, she had dreamed of seeing the lights up close. And now, with Flynn as her guide, Rapunzel had finally left her tower and was travelling to the kingdom. Her dream was about to come true!

Flynn, however, was not happy about the plan. He was a thief. Earlier that morning he had climbed into Rapunzel's tower looking for a place to hide. He was running away from the king's guards because he had stolen a jewelled crown.

Rapunzel had taken the crown and only agreed to give it back if Flynn took her to see the lights. So now Flynn found himself leading her into the very kingdom where he was a wanted man!

If only he could talk her out of it.

Suddenly, he had an idea.

"You know, Blondie," Flynn said quite casually, "the forest can be dangerous. It's no place for someone like you."

Rapunzel frowned. "What do you mean 'someone like me'?" she asked. "Anything you can do, I can do, too. In fact, I'll bet that I can do it better than you!"

"Did you say 'bet'?" Flynn grinned. "Well, why don't we have a contest to see if that's true? If I win, I get my satchel back and you promise to go home."

Rapunzel shook her head. "No, the satchel can't be part of the bet. We have a deal," she pointed out. "The prize should be something else." She thought for a moment. What could the winner get? Then she looked at her chameleon friend, Pascal. He rubbed his tiny green tummy eagerly.

"Oh, I know!" Rapunzel said. She pulled out her iron frying pan and pointed it at Flynn. "Whoever loses has to make the winner a snack."

"You're on, Blondie," Flynn said. He chuckled. It didn't matter. Whatever challenge they decided on, he knew he'd win.

"What kind of contest should we have?" Rapunzel asked. "A painting challenge? A game of chess?"

Flynn scoffed. "This should be a contest of survival," he said. "Remember, it's dangerous out in these woods. For example …" He pointed to a tall tree. "What if a wild animal were chasing us? Who could climb this tree the fastest?" He winked. "Do you think you could beat me?"

Rapunzel squared her shoulders. In a flash, she threw her long hair on to a low branch and swung gracefully up into the tree.

"Hang on!" Flynn cried, dashing after her. "I didn't say go!" He quickly pulled out two arrows and used them to climb up the tree right past Rapunzel.

This is too easy! he thought. *She'll never beat me. I'm the fastest climber in the kingdom.*

When he'd almost reached the top of the tree, Flynn stopped
and looked down. Rapunzel was nowhere in sight. *She's an even
slower climber than I thought!* Flynn said to himself.

Suddenly, from up above, Flynn heard a voice call down.

"Yoo-hoo! Flynn Rider! What took you so long?"

Flynn looked up and gasped. Rapunzel was sitting on the top branch of the tree. "How did you get up there so fast?" he asked.

Rapunzel pointed proudly to her golden hair. "You'd be surprised how much I can do with this," she said. "No branch is too high for my hair to reach."

"That's cheating," Flynn argued. "You can't use your hair to help you. I demand another contest. And this time, no hair."

Rapunzel was disappointed. She didn't like not being able to use her hair. But she didn't need it. She was having so much fun! She agreed to another contest. They decided to have a race next. Pascal would count them down.

"First one to the river wins," Flynn declared.

Pascal gave the signal, and then they were off!

Rapunzel and Flynn sprang forward from the starting line. They ran as fast as they could.

There's no way she'll win this time, Flynn thought. *Her hair can't help her run.*

But as Flynn raced along, he noticed a sign tacked to a tree. WANTED! it said in bold letters. BY ORDER OF THE KING. Flynn's picture was plain to see! But the nose looked slightly off....

"Not again!" Flynn moaned. The WANTED posters always showed him with a fat and crooked nose.

Flynn was staring so hard at the poster that Rapunzel sped right past him. Her gleaming hair trailed behind her.

I can't lose! Flynn thought. He doubled his speed ... and accidentally tripped over Rapunzel's hair. Before he knew it, he was completely tangled in her long locks.

Rapunzel didn't realize what had happened. She kept running and sprinted to the river's edge. She had won!

Rapunzel turned round and smiled. But to her surprise, she saw Flynn wrapped up in her hair.

"That wasn't fair," he panted. "You used your hair again."

"No, I didn't," Rapunzel argued. "I only used my legs."

But Flynn insisted they have one more contest. Rapunzel sighed, then she agreed. After all, she had beaten Flynn twice. Surely she could do it one more time?

Flynn pointed to the wide river in front of them. "Let's see who can cross this first," he said.

Uh-oh, thought Rapunzel. Because she'd never been allowed to leave her tower, she didn't know how to swim. And the river was moving fast!

As Flynn dived into the water, Rapunzel looked around. How could she get across without swimming? Or using her hair?

"Any ideas?" she asked Pascal, who was hanging from a nearby vine. The little chameleon shrugged.

But then Rapunzel's eyes lit up. "That's it!" she said.

Flynn panted as he climbed out of the river. He was dripping wet. "I did it," he said happily. "I won!" Then he looked up, and his jaw dropped.

Rapunzel was standing on the shore, as dry as she had been on the other side.

"I don't understand," Flynn sputtered. "You got here first? And you're not even wet?"

Rapunzel nodded. "That's because I didn't swim across," she said. "I swung across."

"Oh, I see," Flynn said. He shook the water from his hair and grinned slyly. "Then I win! Remember? We made a deal that you couldn't use your hair."

"I didn't use my hair," Rapunzel said. She held up a long, thick vine.
It stretched back all the way to a tall tree on the opposite side of the river. "I
might have learned how to swing on my hair," she said.
"But this time, I used this!" Flynn sighed. He hated to admit it, but
Rapunzel had beaten him. Again. Glumly, he poured the river water out
of his boots. "Fine, you win." He sighed. "Come on, Blondie. It's on to the
kingdom now, I guess."

"Wait. What about the prize?" Rapunzel reminded him. She pulled out
her frying pan. "You owe us a snack. And we're hungry! Aren't we, Pascal?"

"Well, what would you like?" Flynn asked Rapunzel.

"Surprise us!" Rapunzel answered excitedly.

While she and Pascal waited under the cool shade of a cherry tree, Flynn built a fire. Then he began to gather nuts and cherries and cook them. Soon, delicious smells filled the air.

"Mmm!" Rapunzel said, taking a bite. It was one of the tastiest treats she'd ever had.

"You know," Rapunzel told Flynn with a wink, "you might be as good at cooking as I am ... almost."

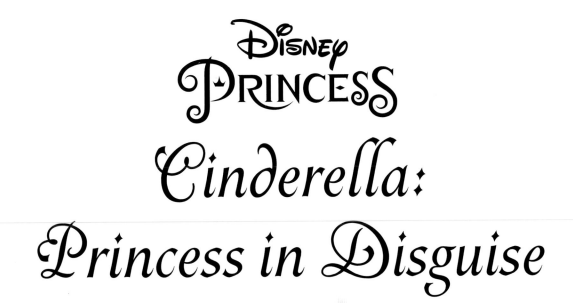

Cinderella:
Princess in Disguise

Cinderella's life had changed overnight. One day, she was cleaning and cooking for her stepmother and stepsisters. The next day, she was married to the Prince and living in a palace.

Cinderella loved living there, but sometimes it felt strange to have the royal staff waiting on her. She wanted to help. In the morning, she would make her own bed before the maids came in to her room.

In the afternoon, she would sometimes invite her maids
to join her for tea.

Most of all, Cinderella wanted to get to know the royal staff
much better. She remembered how lonely she'd been at her
stepmother's house and hoped the maids knew that she was their
friend. But, whenever she tried to chat with them, they would
politely smile and hurry away to finish other chores.

One morning at breakfast, Cinderella told the Prince that she was worried. "I want to make sure the servants are happy working here," she said. "But I can't seem to get any of them to talk to me."

"Wouldn't they tell us if something was wrong?" the Prince asked.

Cinderella nodded. "I suppose so. I just wish there was a way to know for certain."

Later that morning, Cinderella talked with her mouse friends, Jaq and Gus. "There must be something I can do to find out if the staff is happy," she said. "But no one is going to tell me what they really think."

"They would-a talked to you before," Jaq said. "Cinderelly didn't look-a like a princess then."

Suddenly, Cinderella's eyes lit up. "You've just given me an idea!" she said. "Thank you, Jaq!"

First, she went to the costume cupboard and found a wig. Then, she headed straight to the maids' quarters. Luckily, no one was there. A few minutes later, Cinderella came out dressed as a member of the royal staff!

MAIDS

Cinderella walked down the hallway. She hoped no one would recognize her. She hadn't lived in the castle very long, so many of the servants hadn't met her yet. A moment later, she came upon a maid carrying a heavy tub of water.

"Are you new to the castle?" the maid asked when she saw Cinderella. "I don't remember meeting you before."

"Actually, I am," Cinderella answered with a smile. She helped the maid carry the large tub to the centre of the ballroom. "Do you like working here?" Cinderella asked.

"Well, yes," the maid said. She thought for a moment. "But there are some things I would change."

"Like what?" Cinderella asked.

"Like this tub," the maid replied. "If only it were on wheels!"

"Why don't you suggest it?" Cinderella said.

"Oh, the royal family is very busy," the maid said. "I wouldn't want to bother them."

Next, Cinderella headed over to the banquet hall. Some of the royal staff members were busy working at a long table. They chatted happily as they polished the silver.

"Come and join us!" one of the maids called.

Cinderella walked over and examined the gleaming silver. "This looks like it's been polished already," she said.

"It was, just yesterday," the maid replied. "But we're supposed to polish it every day. Rules are rules."

Just then, Cinderella heard a voice coming from down the hall. It was Prudence, the head of the royal household. Cinderella ducked out of sight.

"Excuse me," Prudence said, pulling aside one of the maids. "When you are finished here, I'll need you to polish the back-up silver."

Hmmm, Cinderella thought. She wondered if the royal family even knew they *had* back-up silver. Or that it got polished so often.

When the polishing was finally finished, Cinderella went to the palace's sewing room. She had not met the seamstresses yet. What would they have to say?

When Cinderella entered the room, one of the seamstresses smiled. "Thank goodness Miss Prudence sent some extra help!" she said. "We have to finish all these gowns for the ball on Saturday."

"They're beautiful," Cinderella said, admiring the dresses.

"Gowns are my favourite things to sew," another seamstress chimed in. "Each time I finish one, I imagine what it would be like to wear it. Just once I wish we could go to a ball. I would dance and dance all night long." She sighed.

"What I wish," added another seamstress, "is that we had more light in here. I can barely see the lace I'm stitching!"

Cinderella nodded. With just a few changes, it would be easy to make these wishes come true!

Soon, it was time for lunch. Cinderella followed the maids to the kitchen. She was delighted to see steaming bowls of soup and big slices of crusty bread laid out on a long table.

But just as everyone sat down, a bell rang. The signal meant that one of the royal staff members was needed for a task. A butler at the end of the table got up. He hadn't even had a chance to taste his soup.

How silly! thought Cinderella. *I'm sure it would be easy to plan chores around the staff meals.* Prudence must have known she was interrupting lunch when she rang the bell.

Cinderella slipped away from the kitchen to think. She thought of the maid with her tub of water. She thought of the silver that was polished every day, and the dark sewing room.

The servants were happy working at the palace, but with a few small changes, they could be even happier. And she knew just the way to make that happen. Cinderella smiled. She had some work to do herself!

Quickly, Cinderella went to change back into her own clothes.

But before she could, she bumped into the Prince.

The Prince didn't recognize her at first. But then his eyes grew wide. "Cinderella!" he said in surprise. "Why ever are you dressed like that?"

Cinderella smiled and told him the whole story. "I realized that the only way to make sure the staff was happy was to dress up as a maid myself!" she said. "Fortunately, they didn't recognize me, and they shared the most wonderful ideas about things that would be so easy to change. Let's go and see the King and the Grand Duke. I have so much to tell you all!"

Cinderella changed and then they went to see the King and the Grand Duke.

"I had quite an adventure today," Cinderella told them. "I worked alongside the royal staff. And I got some ideas for small changes that would make a big difference."

"What did you have in mind?" the King asked, curious.

"Well, changing what they work on, for a start," Cinderella replied. "I think they do the same job over and over when they could be doing other jobs that the royal family would truly appreciate. And it would be more interesting for them."

The King nodded thoughtfully. "What a grand idea!" he said. "What else do you suggest?"

That afternoon, Cinderella asked Prudence to gather the royal staff together. "It's nice to see you all again," Cinderella said.

Everyone was confused. No one remembered seeing her earlier that day.

Cinderella held up her disguise. "I was wearing this," she explained. "And I worked alongside you. After hearing what you had to say, we're going to make some changes."

The servants looked at one another nervously.

"From now on," Cinderella said, "all the washtubs will be on wheels, the silver will only be polished when it needs to be, more windows will be added to the sewing room, and your meals will no longer be interrupted."

The royal staff was astonished!

"Oh, and you are all invited to the royal ball on Saturday night." Cinderella smiled. "Does anyone have anything to add?"

"Yes, Princess," a butler said. "Miss Prudence has fainted!"

That Saturday night, Cinderella and the Prince greeted each of the royal staff members by name as they entered the ballroom. Cinderella thanked the seamstresses for the beautiful dress they had sewn for her, the cooks for the delicious food, and the maids for making the castle sparkling clean.

The servants smiled happily as they joined in the dancing. They were growing quite fond of their new princess!

Belle and the
Perfect Pearl

"What do you suppose is behind these doors, Chip?" Belle asked the enchanted teacup.

"Books!" Chip replied.

Belle threw open the doors. "I knew it. More beautiful adventures – tucked away and forgotten," she said.

It wasn't that the Beast didn't use the library. But when he did, he always read the same book.

"My library is your library," the Beast liked to remind Belle. "Read and enjoy any book you find."

It hadn't been long since Belle had agreed to stay at the castle in return for her father's freedom. Each day she was getting to know the Beast better and she was starting to think that he actually cared about her happiness.

So Belle took the Beast at his word and made herself at home in the library. On many days, she spent hours there, reading book after book, losing all track of time.

Belle considered books priceless treasures. So when she took a break from reading, she gave the books special attention. Belle asked Featherduster to help her dust them.

She placed fallen books back on the shelves.

She pressed flat any folded pages.

One morning, Belle noticed the Beast had left his
favourite book lying open on the arm of his chair.
"That's not good for the binding," Belle said.

She picked up the book, closed it, then turned it over in her hands. Although the leather cover was worn, it was a beautiful volume with decorative gems on its brass clasp.

"Chip, look!" she said, pointing at the pearls. There was an empty hole where a fourth one should be.

Hmmm, thought Belle. *How long has it been missing?*

Belle looked around on the floor, in case it had only just fallen out.

Chip helped her search. "I found something!" he called. There by the library door was a single perfect pearl.

"Let's see if it fits," Belle said.

She dropped the pearl
into the hole in the clasp.
"Just right!" said Chip.

But the pearl was loose and wouldn't stay put.

"I have an idea," Belle said. "This book is obviously your master's favourite. I'll fix it up a bit at a time. As the finishing touch, I'll reattach the pearl."

"Then you can surprise him!" Chip said.

Belle nodded. She was happy to do something nice for the Beast.

Belle got right to work. She borrowed some rags and polish from Mrs Potts and gently cleaned the leather cover. Then she put the book back on the Beast's chair so he wouldn't miss it.

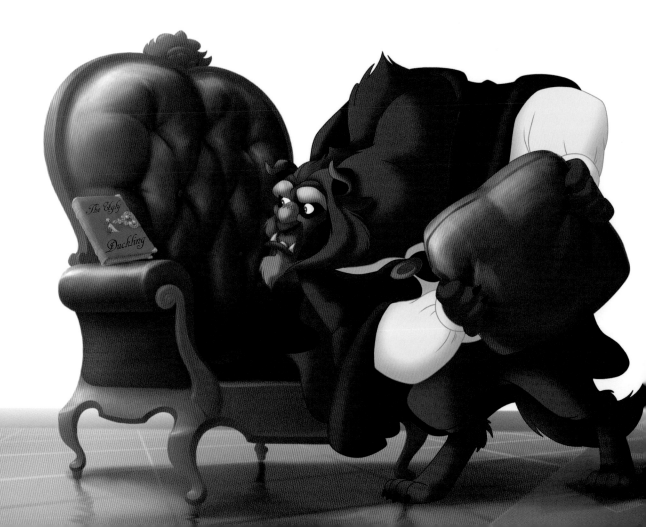

But when the Beast came into the library, he didn't pick up his book. He seemed to be looking for something.

"Can I help?" Belle asked.

"NO!" he bellowed. Then, more quietly, he added, "I mean, no. Excuse me." Without another word, he left the room.

Belle was startled but shrugged it off, assuming the Beast's bad mood would pass.

That afternoon, Belle did some
more work on the book. Carefully,
she smoothed out rumpled pages and
polished the brass clasp.

"I can see myself!" Chip said.

Again, Belle put the book back
in its place on the Beast's chair.

The Ugly
Duckling

Later that evening, Belle passed the
Beast in the hall. She smiled and stopped
to greet him. "Good evening –"
    "Goodnight!" he snapped, hurrying by.
Belle stood there, a bit stunned.
He hadn't even glanced her way.
    Is something the matter? she wondered.

The next morning, it was time for Belle to add the pearl. But she wasn't sure she was ready to give the book to the Beast. He had been so grouchy the day before. *What will he be like today?* she wondered.

Just then, the Beast burst through the door. "You?" he cried. "You've had the pearl all along? I've been looking everywhere trying to find it!"

"Well, why didn't you say so?" said Belle, tossing the pearl on to the table. "By the way, I've been repairing your book as a surprise."

The Beast was shocked.
He looked at the book. He picked
up the pearl. Then he smiled – and
began to laugh.

Belle stormed towards the door.

"Belle, wait," the Beast said. His gentle voice made Belle stop and turn. "I've been working on something for you, too."

In the Beast's hand was a lovely antique brooch.

"It's been in my family a long time," he explained. "I wanted you to have it. But first, I had something to add."

He placed the pearl on the brooch, at the base of the rose. It fitted perfectly.

"I removed the pearl from my book yesterday," he said. "But I must have dropped it on my way out and –" He looked down. "I'm sorry I blamed you."

Now it was Belle's turn to laugh. "Well, I'm sorry I stole your surprise."

Belle pinned the gold rose with the perfect pearl to her dress. Then she watched as the Beast noticed his book's shining brass clasp, polished cover and smooth pages.

"Thank you, Belle," he said. "You've made it new."

Belle and the Beast still had much to learn about one another. But their hearts were in the right place.

Beautiful Colouring

Use your favourite colouring pens or crayons
to make these princess pictures look magical.

Rapunzel's hair is very, very long!

There are always lots of chores to do in the tower.

Some happy whales come to say hello.

Grumpy just can't help being a bit grumpy sometimes!

The children in the village love to hear Belle's stories.

Belle likes to ride with Philippe through the woods.

The ducks look forward to Cinderella's visits.

The Dwarfs learn many things from Snow White.

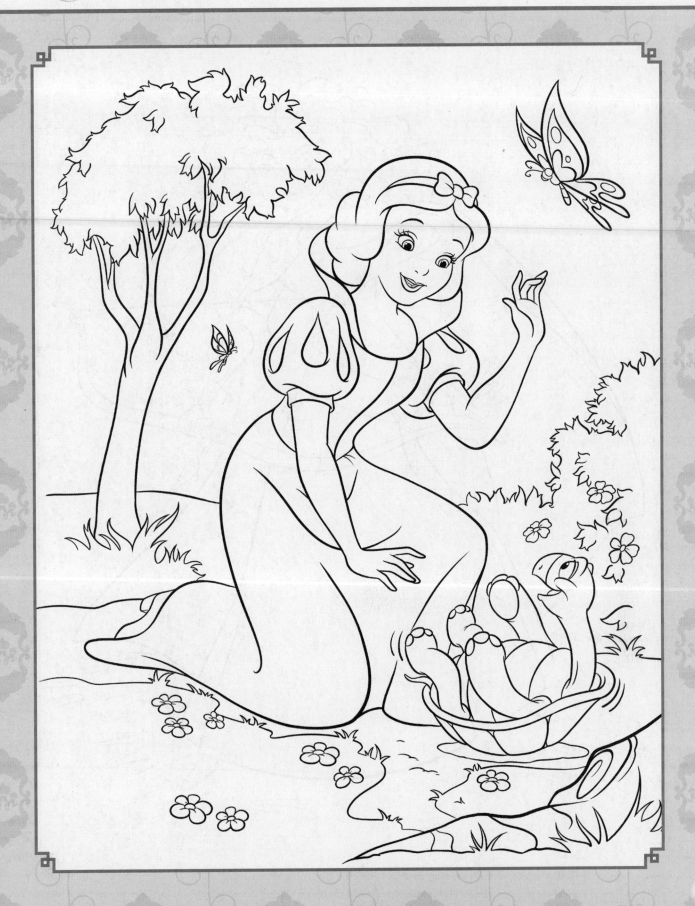

Merida is the best archer in the kingdom.

Flounder cares for his friend Ariel very much.

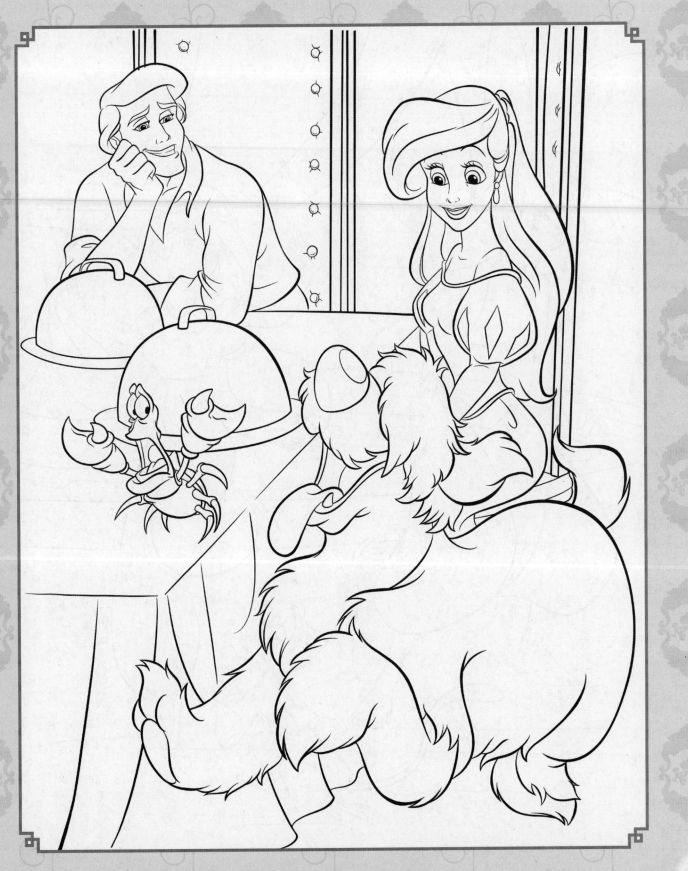

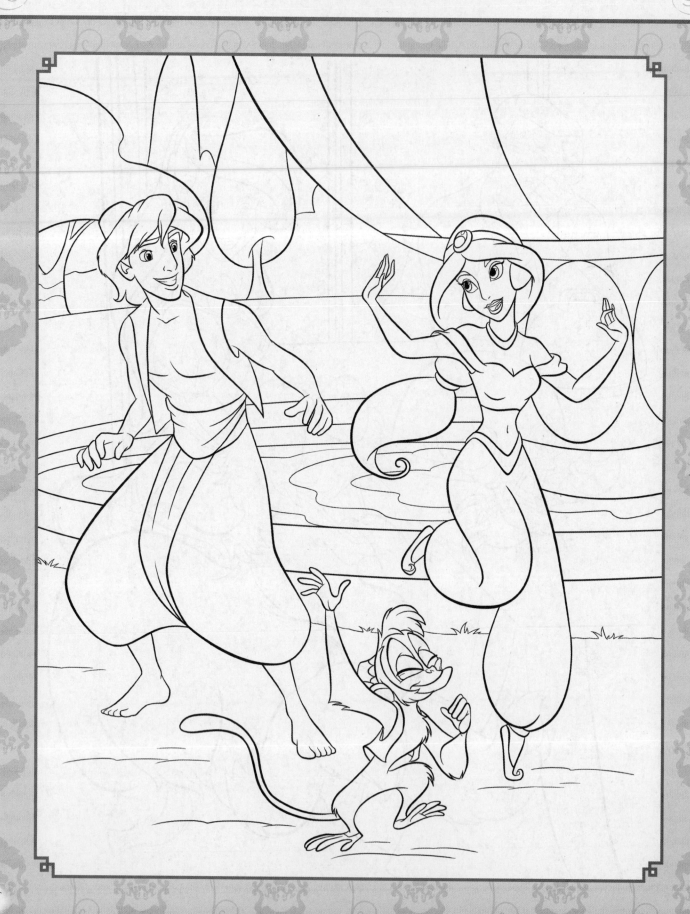

Sugar roses will make Aurora's cake taste delicious.

Charlotte lends one of her pretty dresses to Tiana.

Tiana looks like a princess.

Belle loves her father very much.

The Prince and Belle read their favourite book together.

Cinderella has made a special treat for Jaq's birthday.

These pumpkins will make a perfect pie!

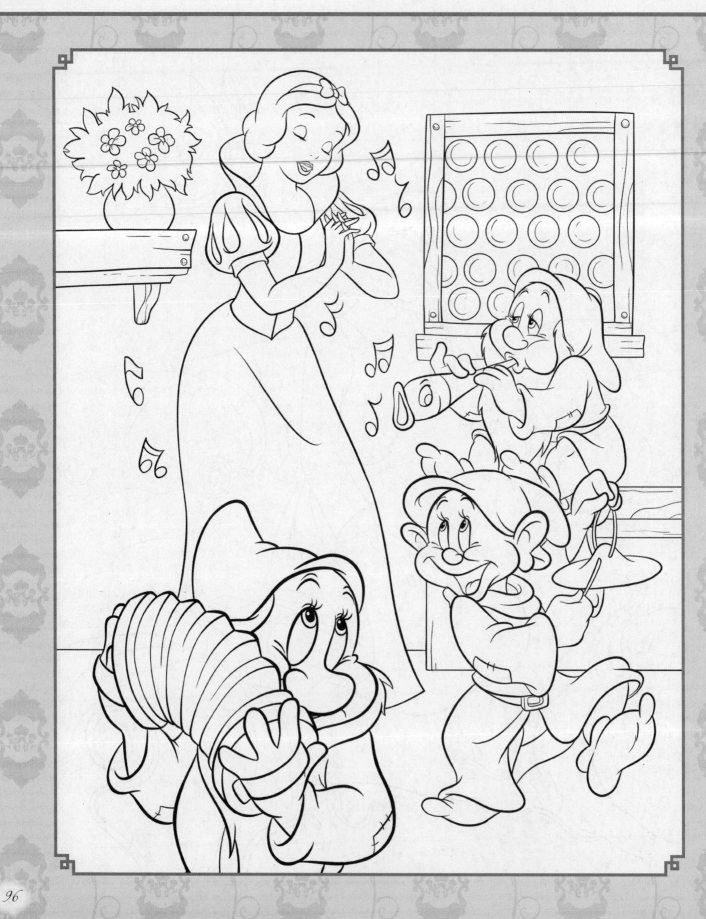

Rapunzel can't believe her eyes as she looks
in the window of the bookshop.

Flynn has brought Rapunzel to the lake
to wait for the floating lights.

Merida can't move in her formal dress!

An arrow from Merida always
hits the target.

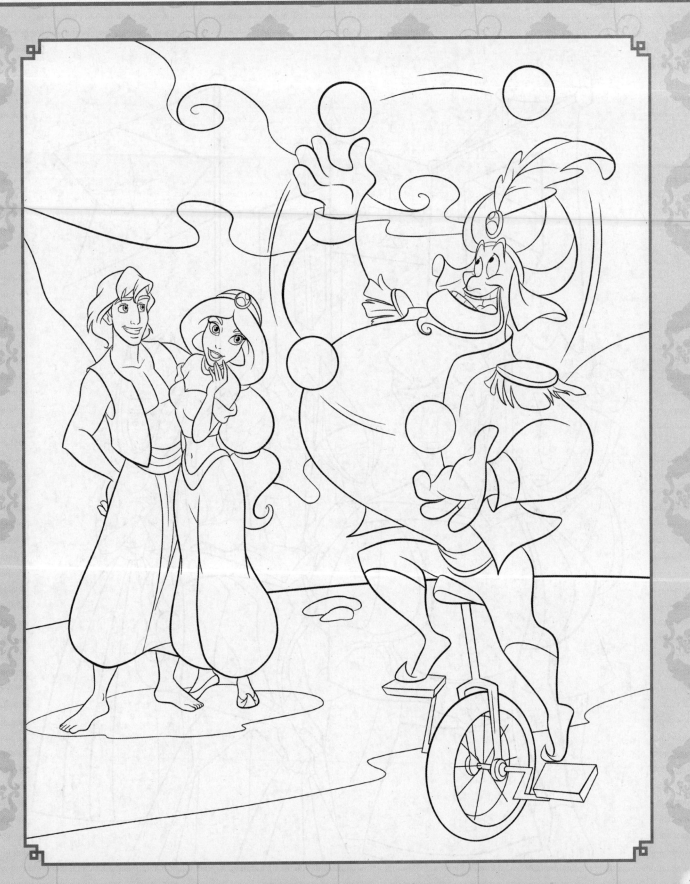

Charlotte and Tiana have been best friends
since they were little girls.

Belle's love broke the spell and turned the Beast
back into a handsome prince.

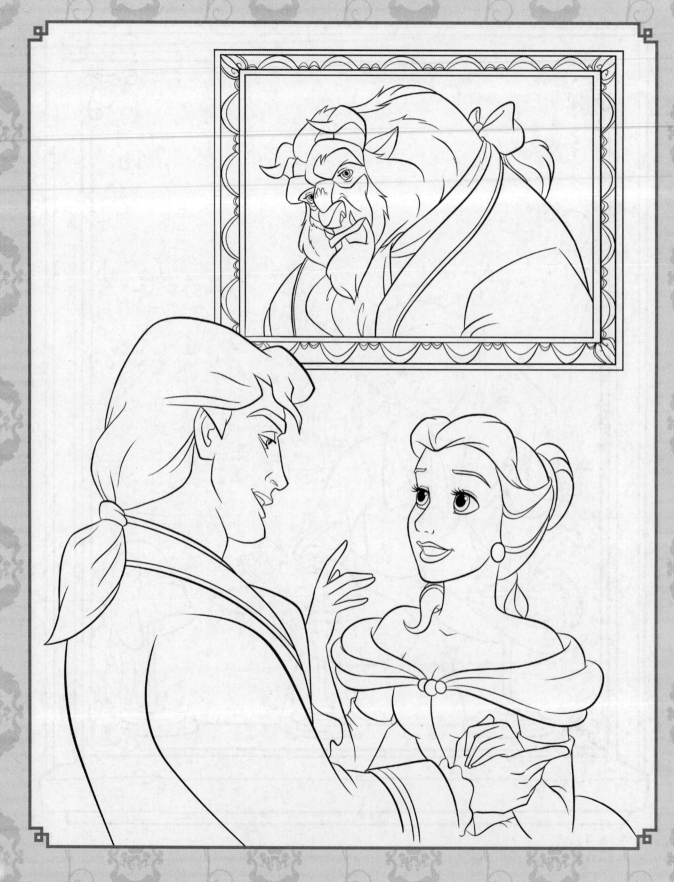

There are lots of things for Belle to buy at the market.

With help from her animal friends,
Cinderella sews a new suit for Prince Charming.

Cinderella's favourite vegetables are broccoli and carrots.

Snow White feeds her bird friends.

Rapunzel is filled with wonder as she looks
at the floating lights up close for the very first time.

Flynn and Rapunzel launch their own lantern into the sky.

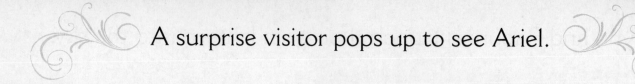

A surprise visitor pops up to see Ariel.

Ariel will never forget her life under the sea.

Merida's favourite thing to do is ride with
Angus through the forest.

Snow White introduces the
Dwarfs to the giants.

The Dwarfs and giants discover that they have lots of things in common.

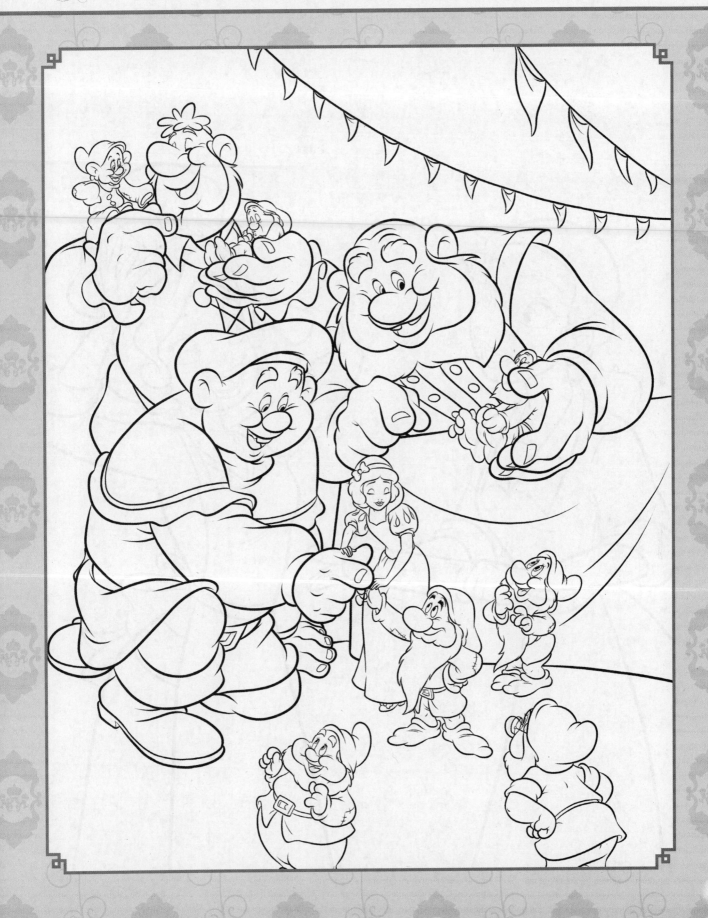

Charlotte wants to help Tiana
make her famous beignets.

The best friends see a wonderful show together.

Merida is teaching Elinor-bear to fish.

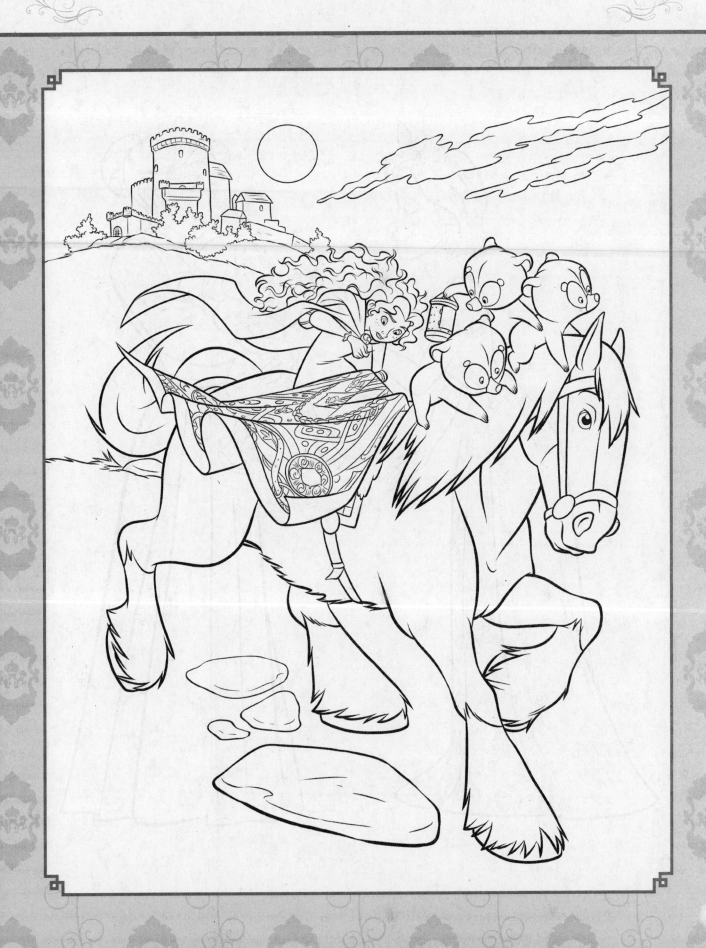

As a reformed thief, Flynn sheepishly returns
the crown to its rightful owner.

Ariel and Flounder love to swim together.

Sebastian and his band give a wonderful concert!

The Sultan loves to see Jasmine happy.

Aurora loves listening to music.

The Dwarfs give Snow White a beautiful sparkling diamond.

Disney
PRINCESS
Enchanting Activities

Complete these princess puzzles and activities,
then turn to page 192 for the answers.

Doc and Dopey are making a necklace for Snow White.
Can you colour it in?

1 = RED   2 = YELLOW   3 = BLUE

140

Hi ho, hi ho. Who is off to work?
Cross out all of the 'I's and 'T's to find out.

1. TDIOIPTEIY _____
2. IBTASITIHTFIUL _____
3. STINEETZIY _____
4. TSLIETEPTIY _____
5. IHTAIIPTPIY _____
6. IGRTIUMTPIY _____
7. TDIITOTIICT _____

Look at this picture of Snow White and her forest friends. Then answer the questions below.

1. How many birds? _____

2. How many butterflies? _____

3. How many rabbits? _____

4. How many squirrels? _____

5. How many turtles? _____

Circle the slipper that matches the one in the Prince's hand.

Draw a picture of yourself at the ball.

Prince Charming's Ball

Find the following words in the pumpkin carriage below.
(Hint: You will find the words going down and across.)

Cinderella
prince
slipper
Gus
midnight
mice
pumpkin
ball
stepmother
gown

a s t d p r s e m g
r m u d r i t s i n
t p r i n c e l d r
s p u m t r p i n r
g u s a b s m p i l
o m i c e r o p g a
w p b a l l t e h i
n k r s t m h r t e
c i n d e r e l l a
r n m p d u r p r w

Help Cinderella's friends finish the surprise. Colour the dress pink, the stars yellow and the hearts purple.

Can you match these sentences with the pictures they describe?
Write the number of each sentence in the
circle beside the correct picture.

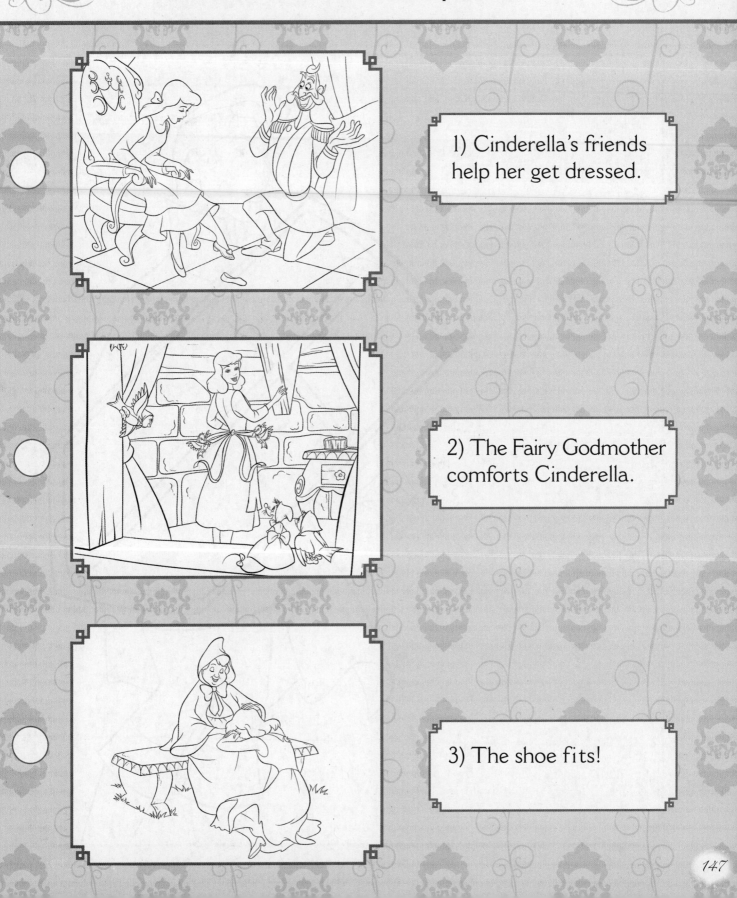

1) Cinderella's friends help her get dressed.

2) The Fairy Godmother comforts Cinderella.

3) The shoe fits!

Prince Phillip is ready to save Princess Aurora.
Connect the dots to reveal his magic sword.

Help Prince Phillip find his way to the castle so he can awaken Princess Aurora with a kiss.

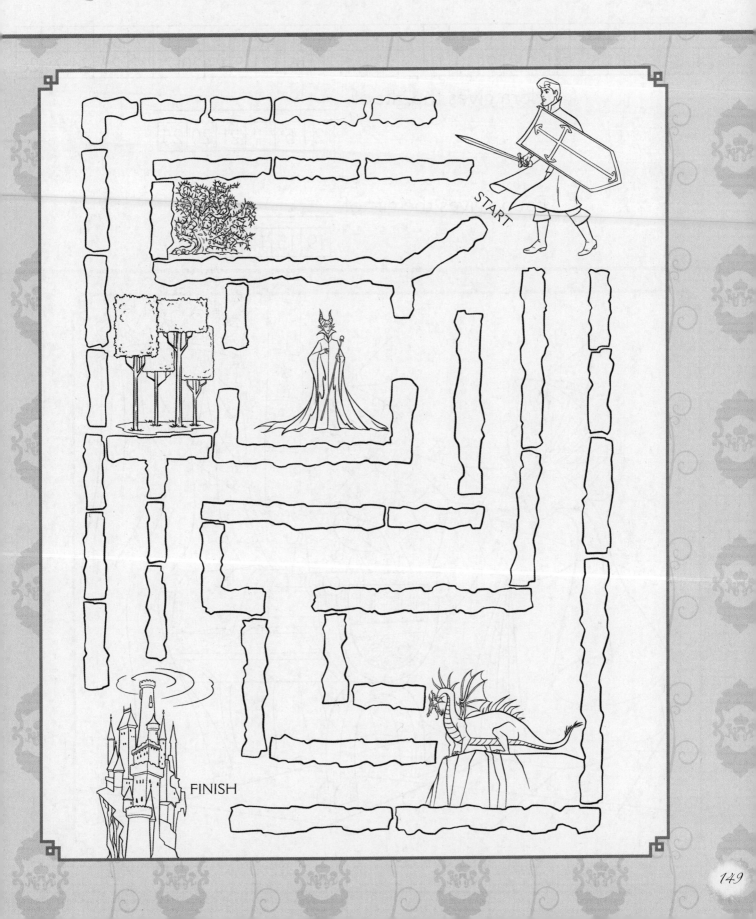

START

FINISH

What gifts do the fairies give to Princess Aurora when she is a baby? Use the code below to find out.

a	b	c	d	e	f	g	h	i	j	k	l	m	n	o	p	q	r	s	t	u	v	w	x	y	z
1	2	3	4	5	6	7	8	9	10	11	12	13	14	15	16	17	18	19	20	21	22	23	24	25	26

Flora gives the gift of _____.

2	5	1	21	20	25

Fauna gives the gift of _____.

19	15	14	7

150

Connect the dots to see Briar Rose's dance partner.

There's magic happening! Can you find seven things that are different in the second picture?

Look at this picture of Ariel, Eric and their animal friends. Then answer the questions below.

1. How many seagulls? ____   3. How many fish? ____

2. How many frogs? ____   4. How many flamingos? ____

Join Ariel as she explores the shipwreck.
Look for the names listed on the right in the puzzle below.
(Hint: You will find them going down and across.)

Prince Eric
Ariel
Flounder
King Triton
Max
Scuttle
Sebastian
Ursula

k r s e a d t c g m p
i e p a z u l l r a r
n o u r s u l a r f i
g d n i u o s s y l n
t e r e p a c r w o c
r l a l d n u o d u e
i s e b a s t i a n e
t d p r e g t s e d r
o r m a x p l t n e i
n i n c s s e d w r c

Eric and Ariel are collecting shells, stones and sticks on the beach. They've arranged them in two different patterns.

Can you finish each pattern by filling in the blank spaces with shells, stones or sticks?

1. 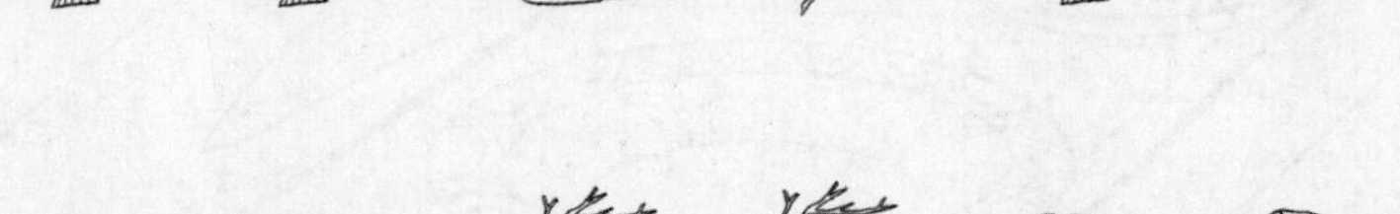 🐚 🐚 🪨 🌿 🐚 🐚 ___ ___ ___

2. 🪨 🪨 🌿 🌿 🐚 🪨 🪨 ___ ___

Everyone in the kitchen wants to cheer Belle up with a show. Find the matching pairs of dishes, cups, forks and knives.

There are six odd and silly things happening in this picture. Can you find them all? Here are some hints:

- What's Gaston wearing on his head?
- There's a fire somewhere.
- Someone is walking on their hands.

- Take a look at Gaston's feet.
- What an odd-looking bicycle!
- An animal has escaped from the farm!

Help Belle and the Beast build a snowman with eyes, arms, a nose and a mouth. Don't forget his hat and scarf!

Be a reader like Belle! Ask an adult to help
you cut along the dotted lines to create two bookmarks.

Let's read
a story
together!

Reading can
take you to
far-off places!

© Disney

© Disney

The Beast's Magic Mirror lets you see anyone you want.
Draw the person you would like to see in the Magic Mirror.

Write the types of the animals and objects below in the crossword puzzle.

Across

1 4 6 7 8

Down

2 3 4 5

Can you find the following 10 objects hidden in the picture below?

- A glove
- A beach ball

- A cockerel
- A handbag
- A brush

- A cake
- A broom
- A pair of boots

- A comb
- A car

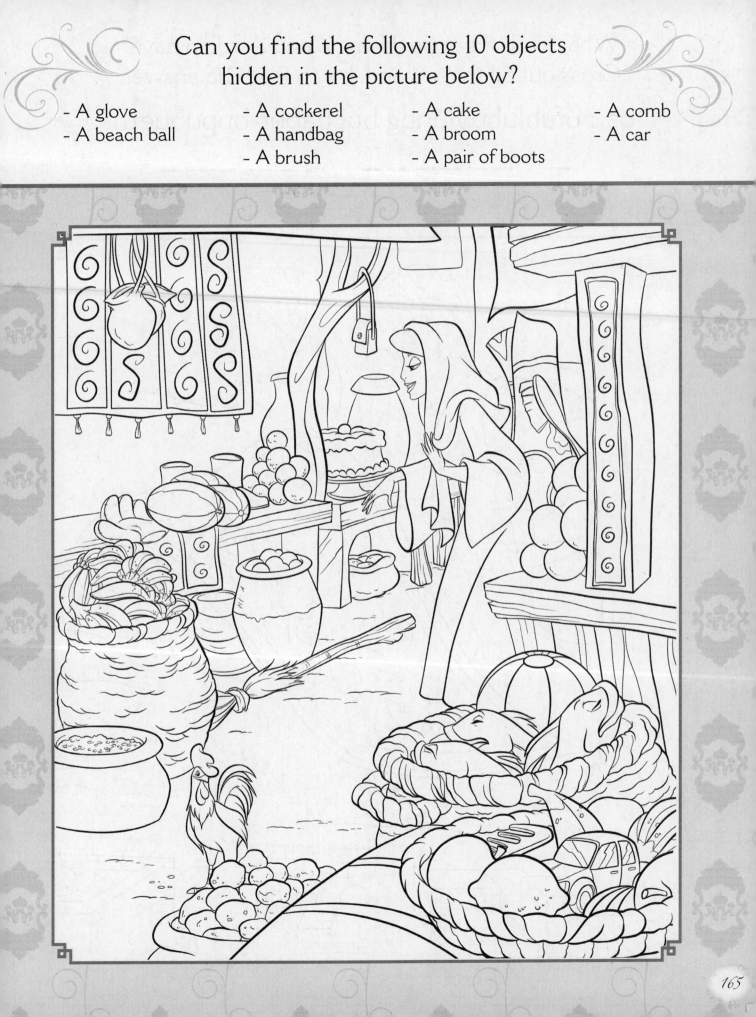

What kind of pet do Jasmine and Aladdin have?
Cross out all the 'u's and 'b's to find the answer.

bau ufublubuyiunbg bucuabur-bupubuetb!

_ _____ ___-___

166

Jasmine and Aladdin are ready for a reading adventure!
Ask an adult to help you cut along the dotted lines
to create two bookmarks.

Read a book
and discover
a whole new
world!

Every book
holds a new
adventure!

© Disney

© Disney

Use crayons or colouring pens to colour in
the palace and the city of Agrabah.

Jasmine wore the same outfit and accessories twice this week.
Which two days did she wear the same things?
_____ and _____

Look at this picture of Pocahontas, John Smith and their woodland friends. Then answer the questions below.

1. How many deer? _____
2. How many squirrels? _____
3. How many rabbits? _____
4. How many raccoons? _____

Help Pocahontas find her way through the forest to John Smith.

How many butterflies do you see in the picture?
Write the number below.

I see _____ butterflies.

Meeko is hidden four times in the picture below. Can you find him?

Complete this scene using the small pictures below.
Write the letter of each picture in the correct white box.

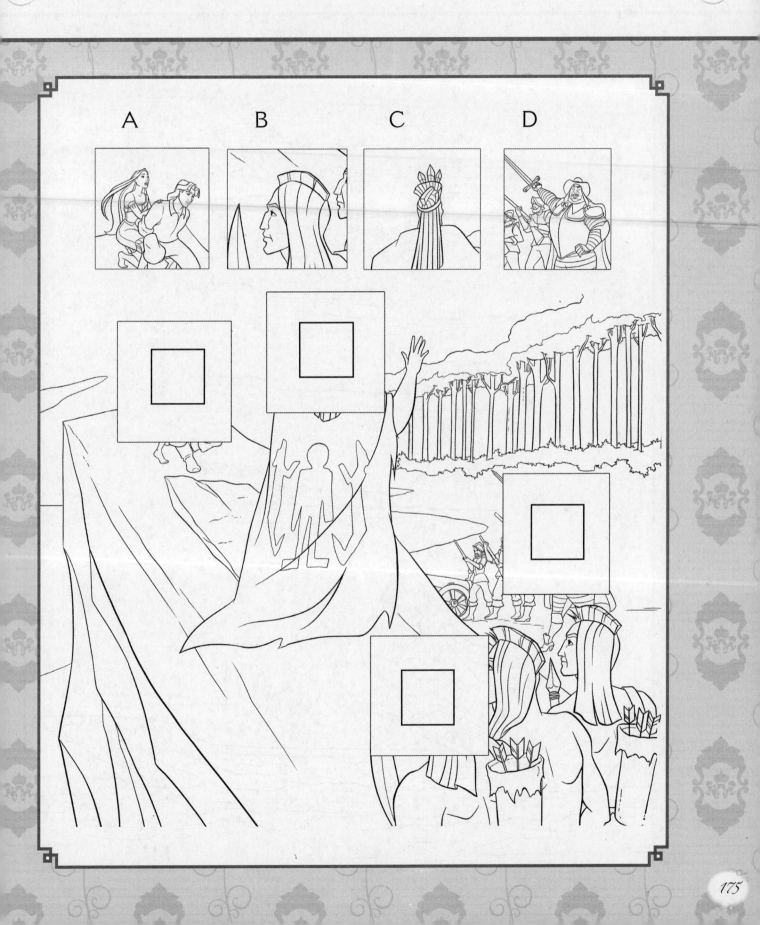

Only one of the canoes matches Pocahontas's canoe. Which one is it?

Write the types of the animals and objects below in the crossword puzzle.

Across

2

5

6

Down

1

3

4

Mulan needs to get to the Emperor. Can you help her?

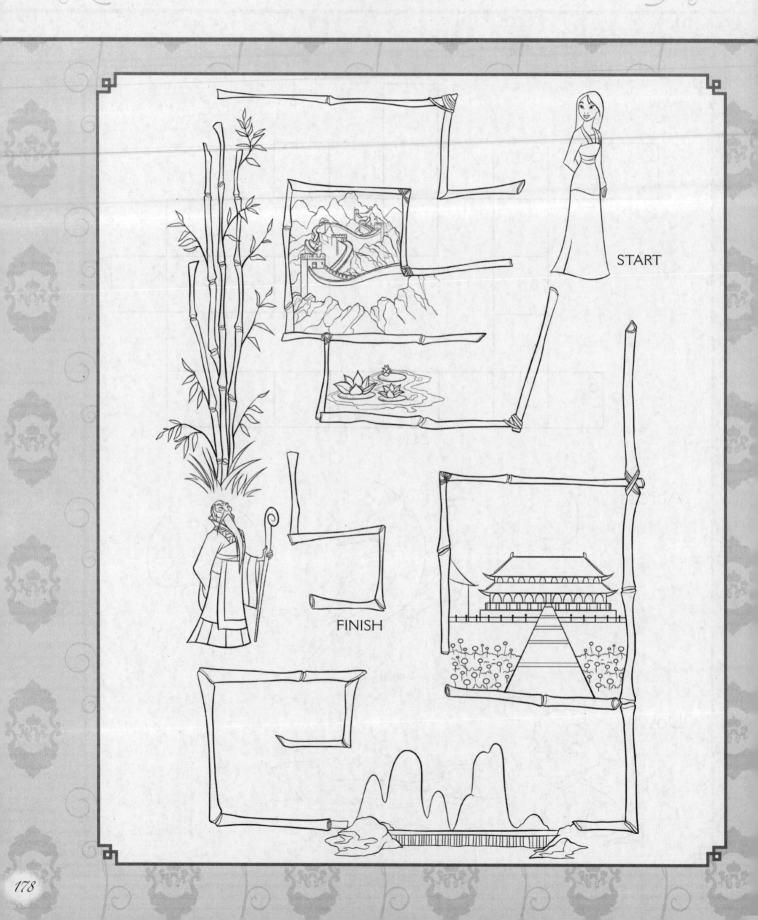

START

FINISH

Help Shang train his men. Can you find
five things that are different in the second picture?

Complete this scene with the small pictures below.
Write the letter of each picture in the correct white box.

A

B

C

Help the Matchmaker find the two Mulans that are exactly the same.

Write the types of the people and things below in the crossword puzzle.

Across

3 [horse]

5 [old woman]

7 [man with cane]

Down

1 [dragon]

2 [sword]

4 [saddle]

6 [girl]

Ask an adult help you cut out each picture, punch a hole at the top and thread a ribbon through the hole. Then decorate your room with these beautiful princesses!

Draw a picture of yourself as a princess on the back of the decorations.

© Disney

© Disney

© Disney

© Disney

Each of the rows below must have four princesses:
Snow White, Aurora, Cinderella and Belle.
Fill each empty box with the correct letter.

Draw a line from each princess to her shadow.

Ask an adult to help you cut out each picture, punch a hole at the top and thread a ribbon through the hole. Then decorate your room with these beautiful princesses!

Draw a picture of yourself as a princess
on the back of the decorations.

© Disney

© Disney

© Disney

© Disney

"Mirror Mirror on the wall, who is the fairest one of all?"
Draw yourself in the mirror.

Prince Charming and Cinderella
take Bruno for a brisk walk.

Ask an adult to help you cut out each picture, punch a hole at the top and thread a ribbon through the hole. Then decorate your room with these beautiful princesses!

Draw a picture of yourself as a princess on the back of the decorations.

© Disney

© Disney

© Disney

© Disney

"Mirror Mirror on the wall, who is the fairest one of all?"
Draw yourself in the mirror.

Prince Charming and Cinderella
take Bruno for a brisk walk.

The Fairy Godmother joins Cinderella for tea and a chat.

Answers

Page 141
1. Dopey, 2. Bashful,
3. Sneezy, 4. Sleepy,
5. Happy, 6. Grumpy,
7. Doc.

Page 142
1. 4 birds, 2. 4 butterflies,
3. 3 rabbits, 4. 2 squirrels,
5. 1 turtle.

Page 143

Page 145

Page 147

Page 149

Page 150
Flora gives the gift of Beauty.
Fauna gives the gift of Song.

Page 151

Page 153

Page 155
1. 2 seagulls, 2. 3 frogs,
3. 4 fish, 4. 3 flamingos.

Page 156

Page 157

Page 158

Page 159

Page 164

Page 165

Page 166
A flying car-pet.

Page 170
Tuesday and Thursday.

Page 171
1. 3 deer, 2. 4 squirrels,
3. 2 rabbits, 4. 1 raccoon.

Page 172

Page 173
I see 15 butterflies.

Page 174

Page 175

Page 176
C matches Pocahontas's canoe.

Page 177

Page 178

Page 179

Page 180

Page 181
7 and 9.

Page 182

Page 185

Page 186

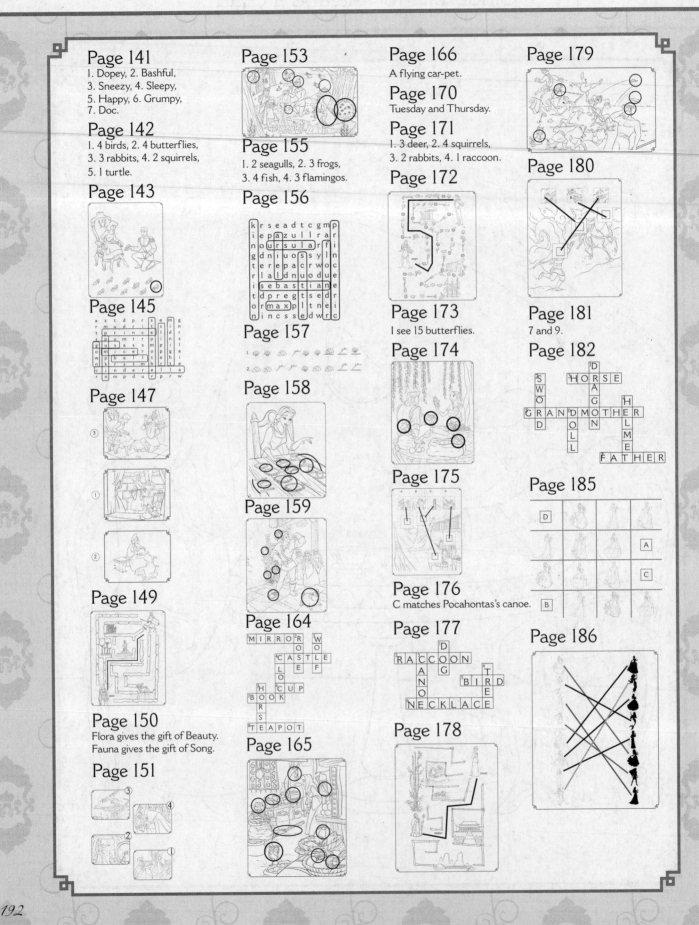